Trauma Triggers:
Triumphs & Scleroderma

I Decided

Monika Hilton

Imprint Productions, Inc.

I Decided

ISBN: 978-1-956884-14-2

Contributing Editor: All services completed by Imprint Productions, Inc.
Cover Design: All services completed by Imprint Productions, Inc.

Printed in the United States of America
Published by Imprint Productions, Inc.
First Edition 2023

Contact: **info@imprintproductionsinc.com**
Visit Us: **www.imprintproductionsinc.com**

Imagine

Imagine fulfilling your passion with the career of a lifetime, working your dream job for more than 20 years. Imagine rising to Stardom as a reputable chef and cake artist and twice competing on national television. Then, you are diagnosed with this condition that tightens your skin, stiffens your joints, and robs your hands of mobility and range of motion.

Your career is over!

That condition is called Scleroderma, an autoimmune disease that causes hardening of the skin and potential problems in blood vessels, internal organs, and the digestive tract.

In this book, I will intimately depict how Scleroderma affected me physically, mentally, and spiritually after the diagnosis. I will also reveal compilations of Traumas, Triggers, and Triumphs I endured throughout my life. Grieving the murder of my mother, surviving COVID-19 twice, battling feelings of worthlessness, and SCLERODERMA all sent me into this dark place. A place I kept buried inside. No one knew I was there, so no one could help pull me out. It was between me and God, and it was only up to me to get out.

"I Decided" I did not want to curl up and die! "I have a lot of Mo living to do, and I'm gonna do just that."

"I Decided" to be intentional about making improvements in my mental health, my dietary health, and my physical health. In addition to prayer and meditation, I started incorporating affirmations into my daily routine. When I began to speak positively to myself at the start of my day, it carried me throughout the day. When I changed the foods I had been eating all my life, my mood, blood pressure, and energy improved significantly.

When **"I Decided"** nothing was more important than my health and wellness, I stopped making excuses and began incorporating physical therapy into my schedule twice a week. I gained a little Mo pep in my step one day at a time.

"I Decided" was written to encourage readers. Quitting is not an option! Remain fearless and faithful, even in the midst of the storm.

-MO HILTON

"My Life Experience with Scleroderma Disease."

Contents

INTRODUCTION

I was born in Lexington, North Carolina, in 1976. As a youngster, I had a vision of my name in the lights, like on the marquee on Broadway. As I got older, that vision stuck with me. I saw my name in lights at the Apollo Theater in New York City and the Fox Theater in Atlanta. This image has always been my fuel.

I was lucky to have that vision because it inspired me. As I journeyed through life, my vision started to take hold. I had become a chef and a baker with an excellent reputation for intricate and beautiful cake designs. My vision continued taking hold throughout my career and became apparent when I was selected to compete on two national cooking shows on television.

But that vision, built on determination and success, came crashing down because I was diagnosed with Scleroderma, an autoimmune connective tissue and rheumatic disease that causes inflammation in the skin and other areas of the body. In addition to terrible physical pain, I could not hold a kitchen utensil like a spatula or spoon. I ask you to imagine being unable to hold a spatula or spoon for yourself ... and that was me, an accomplished and recognized chef and cake artist. Very tough. A considerable setback to overcome.

After a journey with doctors, depression, body pain, and physical disabilities, and tremendous support from my husband, children, and God, I am seeing my name in lights again, but not as a baker or chef. I have pivoted to something else. I'm in a new chapter in my life and a new approach to seeing my name in the lights.

This is my story.

Sincerely,

Monika "Mo" Hilton

DEDICATION

"When life throws you lemons, make lemonade" is a legendary phrase that encourages optimism and a positive can-do attitude in the face of adversity or misfortune.

Lemons suggest sourness or difficulty in life; making lemonade turns them into something sweet, positive, or desirable.

My mom taught me about turning negative situations into positive ones.

When life throws you lemons, make lemonade, she would say...

Be Grateful

Things may seem daunting initially, but if you consider all the good things you have going on in your life versus what's not going so well, you'll realize that all the small things you have to be grateful for outweigh the bad.

Stay Calm

I have learned to take deep breaths to help me relax when life gets to be too much. Despite the issues in your life, it's important not to worry. Instead, react positively when a problem occurs; your reaction is the only thing you can control. Indeed, there are other factors, but it is up to you to have a positive thought process to de-escalate the situation instead of not dealing with it or making it worse.

Learn to Accept Things

You make your problems worse if you push them away without addressing them. I often ask God to "Grant me the serenity to accept the things I cannot change, courage to change the things I can and the wisdom to know the difference." (Reinhold Niebuhr)

Meditate

I've learned that daily meditation helps keep me grounded. Try it! In the past, for many years of dealing with adversity, I would pray and keep it moving. Sometimes I had nothing to say to God; I'd sit quietly and relax my mind and body. I never realized I was actually meditating; I didn't call it that. When a significant problem in your life occurs, sometimes, your immediate response is too soon.

During these times, you need to pray, then sit silently until God says move. Or be still and allow the storm to pass without worrying and panicking. Meditation is like already having your sugar water ready, just in case a bunch of lemons is thrown your way.

Be A Warrior

Face your problems with the characteristics of a warrior. There is strength in dealing with whatever is happening in your life; it boldly screams CONFIDENCE! You can test your true power and growth if you utilize the opportunity to do so with a warrior mindset. This allows you to face these challenges with strength, courage, and determination.

I mentioned to you in my first book about my struggle with having Scleroderma. I almost allowed this disease to get the best of me. "But God!"

I was afraid of everything I had learned about the disease and automatically applied ALL of the symptoms to my case. I stopped leaving my house, taking pictures, recording videos, and writing. There were times I didn't even get out of bed. My body was changing so rapidly that I almost gave up!

One day momma came by my house to check on me. She had been calling me, but I didn't know she called because my phone had died. I knew it was dead, but my charger was downstairs, and I didn't want to get out of bed to get it. It was after 12 pm, and Momma didn't like anyone being in bed after 12 pm unless they didn't feel well. She knocked on my bedroom door but didn't wait for an answer because she knew Marvin, my husband, wasn't there, so she just walked in. Looking in my face, she asked, "*Hey Deah, you up?*"

I said, "*Yes, ma'am.*"

She said, with concern in her voice, "I called you, and you didn't pick up. How are you feeling?"

I responded, "*I'm ok.*"

She looked at me and then asked, "If you're ok, why are you still in the bed? You need to get up, wash and put some clothes on! Go for a walk, sit outside on the porch, and get some sun! You cannot lay around in this bed all day, every day; you're going to make your situation worse! Didn't the doctor say, "You must continue to stretch and exercise?"

I said, "Yes, but I am so stiff, it hurts to exercise, and the sun burns my skin." Then I broke down and started crying.

Momma sat beside me on the side of my bed and said, "Nikki, I know you are hurting, and it breaks my heart that you are going through this, but God did not bring you this far to leave you! Even though what you are experiencing has changed your physical abilities, it has not changed your capabilities. Be Grateful this is not as bad as it could be."

Sounding like the doctor, she continued breaking down the disease, "Systemic Scleroderma has been known to attack people's organs and cause lung, heart, and\or kidney failure, in addition to skin issues and joint stiffness. You are only experiencing the latter two. Somebody else is doing much worse."

I lay there listening to my momma minister to me as she said, "Stay Calm! Didn't the doctor tell you that stress exacerbates your symptoms? Stop crying and talk to me. Stop trying to carry all this by yourself. I am here for you, just like Marvin. Learn to accept the things that you cannot change. God chose you for this assignment for a reason. Get back on your mission and spread awareness about Scleroderma. Somebody somewhere is feeling the same pain as you, and they don't know why, or their doctor is treating them for something totally different."

She looked at me with determination and said, "You have already begun to help change the way people pay attention to their family illnesses, make healthier choices, even ask better questions when they go to the doctor. You have been an inspiration to so many. Ain't no way I'm gonna let you give up! I know you pray, but do you ever stop thinking? Be still and wait on God. Meditate, just clear your mind, relax your body, and value your solitude."

Momma said, "You can do this; I know I raised a fighter, a warrior! Things will get better when you believe they will. Faith without works is dead; if you don't get up outta this bed and get moving, don't be mad if the stiffness persists."

Life had thrown Momma so many lemons throughout her 66 years. Until then, I never understood how she survived her many obstacles and seemed calm. Her mission was not to let me, my brothers, or anyone see her sweat.

I began to apply all those points to my daily life choices. In doing so, I resumed making my live videos on Facebook, and Momma joined me in some of them. I completed "The Mo Experience: Autobiography and Cookbook." I even bottled my seasonings and sauces so my supporters could genuinely have and enjoy "The Mo Experience" in their kitchens.

Momma was extremely proud of "The Mo Experience: Autobiography and Cookbook," perhaps even more than I did. She'd say she wanted to be the first to purchase her VIP book package, "Hot off the press!" She made sure everyone knew she paid the regular price for everything she got from me, which was her way of supporting her "baby's" dreams.

I made my first cake around 1998. It was nothing fancy. One day, Marvin and I just had a taste for a vanilla cake to accompany our Sunday dinner. It was so good. I called Momma over to get a slice. It was a French Vanilla box cake. I did not put anything different from what the box said, but that cake was delicious! Momma thought so, too; we devoured that cake in one day.

The following week she called me to see if I would make another cake for Sunday dinner. I did, and she helped us eat that one too. That was my beginning. I began making cakes more frequently when we had a taste for cakes and for my sons' birthdays, and before I knew it, I was selling cakes to co-workers and friends. Momma was right there, encouraging me to my highest potential.

In 2000, I became a legit home-based business DBA "The Cake Lady." In 2003 I opened my first bakery storefront, and Momma was there every step of the way! In fact, for the next 20 years, Momma would make it her business to be wherever I was so that she could support every milestone I reached in my career.

Hearing Momma say, "That's My Baby," with her beautiful, loving smile felt so good.

"Momma, on July 6, 2020, my heart was shattered, and my world was forever changed when you were maliciously taken away from us. I didn't think I could continue without you, Momma, but I remembered never seeing you defeated! You always showed so much poise, courage, and strength, and in my mind, I wanted to do the same for my family, but I was not as strong as I thought you were. You would be happy to know that Marvin is very strong, just like when you were with us. He is still taking care of your baby."

This book is dedicated to you, Momma!

MO'S EARLY EXPERIENCES

I was born Monika Lanette Ricks in Lexington, North Carolina, on September 25, 1976. Lexington is in the central part of the state, about twenty miles from Winston-Salem.

My parents were Larry and Dorothy A. Ricks (Pompey). My mom was born in Manning, South Carolina, and my dad was born in Lexington, North Carolina.

They had three kids together, two boys and a girl. My oldest brother, Charles, was born before they got married. Once they were married, they had Dwayne, Darius, and me. I was my mom's youngest and the only girl in our family, but dad had two more sons, RaShard and Marcus, from his second marriage to Carrie.

My parents only stayed together briefly. They married in 1972 and were separated by the time I was three years old, around 1979. Though estranged, I developed a long-distance relationship with my younger brothers, seeing them sometimes in the summer, but we didn't bond until we got older.

After my parents separated, we moved a lot. We moved to a small town called Benson, North Carolina, about one hundred miles from Lexington. My dad and his family stayed in Lexington. Dad passed away in 2014, but my Stepmom and brothers are still in that area.

Sometimes at Christmas, but not always, Daddy would take us Christmas shopping. He usually came by himself. But there were too many years when he did not visit us at all. He would send some money in the mail.

Over the years, my mom and dad made several attempts at co-parenting. Momma was the custodial parent and did all the teaching and discipline. When we saw our younger brothers, it seemed like they lived so well, and we had so little. They had bicycles, computers, electric trains, and toys we didn't have when we were coming up. Mama was raising us mostly by herself. Although I grew up developing a loving relationship with my stepmom, I never got the opportunity to have those adult conversations with my dad before he lost his speech from MS complications. He never really poured positive attributes into my life to help cultivate my healthy future with financial literacy, emotional stability, social skills, the importance of education, and just life lessons in general. He didn't protect me from physical abuse and molestation.

I don't think he believed the fighting was as bad as it was. Maybe he took it as brother-sister quarrels, but our fights got way more serious than that. And I never told him about the molestation. We never had serious or intimate conversations, so I didn't know how to initiate anything that serious. We never talked about birds and bees nor dollars and cents. I don't even recall Dad saying he loved me. When I would say, "I love you, Daddy!" He'd respond, "Yep," and that was it! I was fortunate to marry a man like Marvin, flaws, and all, because my dad never taught me how a man should treat their "Baby Girl." After 33 years of "life'n" together, Marvin and I figured some things out, and he treats me like a queen.

Enough is Enough!

As an infant, my brother Darius was killed in an automobile accident. He was two years old. I was only a few months old when this happened. It was a traumatic experience for the family. He had epilepsy and was having a seizure, and out of panic, after failed attempts at getting help from neighbors, my mom tried to rush him to the hospital on icy roads in January 1977.

Darius never made it to the hospital. He was killed instantly in the crash when momma slid head-on into a tree. Momma was in a coma for several months after that horrific accident. After she came out of the coma, she was paralyzed on the right side of her body. Her doctors told her she would never walk again… but I had a praying grandmama!

I remember the emotional pain it caused Momma when she talked about it. It was as vivid as if I had memories of that fateful day. My brother Dwayne harbored terrible feelings towards our mother because he blamed her for the accident for a long time. He took his frustrations out on me too. Dwayne and Darius were almost a year apart. Remember I said we were all September babies? Dwayne was born September 8th, Darius September 4th, and I was born September 25th; as fate would have it, Marvin's birthday is September 12th.

Dwayne, "Mont" is what we called him, short for his middle name, LaMont, who was a bully! He tormented me most of my adolescent life. I'm not talking about Mont teasing me or pushing; this was severe unfair fist fights! Unless you were Ali or Frazier, no one, let alone a little girl, should have endured the busted lips, body slams, bruises, and black eyes I got from my brother. Trust me; he did not hold back because I was a girl and his baby sister.

I wasn't the only one Mont would get physical with. He would fight anyone! He was often suspended from public schools and even sent to reformatory schools. That's what they used to call them, and now they are called alternative schools. Mont would be ready to go toe to toe with anyone, big or small. Our oldest brother Charles got into fights with him when Charles would take up for me. He fought with Momma's boyfriend too. They would say, "Mont leave that girl alone, pick on somebody your own size," and he'd take that as an invitation.

The terrorizing and bullying did not stop until I decided, *I am sick of this s-h-i-t; I am going to stand up for myself.* Once I did that, he eased up on that. I was about eleven or twelve when I finally fought back.

I was sitting in the car one day listening to some cassette tapes. He came outside and said, "Momma said to come in the house and stop running up her battery." I didn't listen because I didn't believe my mom said that because she knew I was outside listening to the music. But he wanted to control me and be the boss; he wanted to sit in the car and listen to music.

He returned and told Mama, "Nikki is outside playing in the car."

Trying to be neutral, Mama came to the door and yelled impulsively at me, "Get outta my car!" I gathered all the tapes, exited the car, and entered the house. When I got inside, he was standing behind the door. He corner-popped me with a towel, and it really hurt. My first instinct was to turn around to see where that pain originated. He stood behind the door with a white towel and an evil smirk. I had all the cassette tapes in my hand, and I just threw them at him, and they hit him in the head. The cassettes caused a cut on the top of his forehead. When he saw that blood on his head, he punched me so hard it knocked me out. I must have been out for a while because when I came to, the police were there.

My mom had called the police on him. She had issues with him too many times and finally said, "ENOUGH IS ENOUGH!" His bad behavior started as early as elementary school. Many more times, my brother tormented me as if he hated me.

Whenever my mom was getting dressed up, especially Friday and Saturday nights, and putting on makeup, I knew she was about to go out. That meant I would be left with my brother, which was not good for me. He stayed at home because he only had a few friends. He was a homebody and stayed to himself.

I felt that his ultimate reason for living was to terrorize me for whatever reason. When I finally stood up for myself, after the time when the police came, he eased up and left me alone. I think that's what it took. I had to show him, "Look, dude, I'm not scared of you; just stop hitting me." I never knew what triggered him to be so violent. I remember Momma regularly took him to a psychiatrist at a mental health facility, but we never discussed those appointments. Mont lived in the fast lane, dealing drugs and going in and out of jail, so we never got to have an adult heart-to-heart conversation about our relationship. He was killed in a motorcycle accident in 2004.

Betrayed by Someone I Trusted

When I was about nine or ten years old, I was molested by my uncle, my mom's brother. This was in Benson, North Carolina. He would come to the house and pick me up. He would lure me in by saying, "Come on, Nikki, ride with me to Vanessa's house, then we'll go to the store and get you some candy." Vanessa was my momma's baby sister. I would go to see my cousins, Tonia and Shanda. Although it was not rape (he never entered inside of me), it was sexual abuse and a traumatic experience that no child should go through. He used to touch me between my legs and put my hands on his penis.

I remember he took me to his girlfriend Gail's house once. I thought I was going there to see my baby cousin, but Gail and the baby weren't there when we arrived. He said he was going to take a shower and then take me home. I was sitting in the living room looking at the TV. He undressed in the bedroom and came out with a towel wrapped around his waist. I acted like I didn't see him by not reacting, but I knew that was inappropriate. I grew very uncomfortable because of what he had already done to me. I had butterflies in my stomach, and I just wanted my momma! When I heard the shower stop, my anxiety grew heavy. The bathroom door opened. I continued to play it cool like I was looking at tv, but then I noticed out of the corner of my eyes that he walked out of the bathroom butt ass naked!!!

I screamed, "ILLK!!! "Where are your clothes?" I knew this was no accident. He was testing me to see what else he could get away with. I said, "You are nasty!"

He said, "I left my towel in the room"!

I said, "No you didn't; Imma tell my momma!" That's when he tried to get serious with me. He threatened to tell my momma I was being fresh and walked in on him when he was in the room getting dressed. Why was I exposed to such filth at that age and by someone I trusted?

As a fear tactic, he would tell me, "If you tell your mom or anyone, you will get in a lot of trouble." That was scary because my mom was a no-nonsense type of parent. I believed that if I said anything, I would get a whooping from my mom and him. My uncle would say it many times to me. This was the last time I ever got in the car with him again.

What did I do? I kept my mouth shut and endured the trauma. I buried this trauma in the back of my mind for many years. I would ask Tonia and Shanda if he ever picked them up to take them to the store, and they would say no, he won't even give us $.50.

Almost ten years later, when I was nearly twenty years old, I found the courage to tell my mom what had happened to me from her brother. I had been watching the television show "America's Most Wanted." That was the John Walsh show. An episode told the story of two girls (18 and 19 years old) who accused their father of sexually molesting them. Watching this episode and thinking about it and the trauma I encountered and buried gave me the courage to tell my mother.

I told her about what her brother had done to me, and my mom was shocked when she heard about the abuse. We talked, well...I talked, but she just sat there silent, with tears in her eyes. She never confronted him. I also told my oldest brother Charles. This was when I was in my 30's. He pretty much responded like my momma did. Hurt by the thought of an uncle doing something like this to me but not hurt enough to say anything. Although he said he would confront him, I don't think he ever did! He didn't protect me either. When I told my husband what had happened, even though it was many years from when this happened, he was furious; he wanted to confront my uncle and my mom. But I didn't give it the power to bring me down. I tucked it back where I had it buried for so many years. I was devastated that I didn't get the same response from my mom, whom I've always lived with. She's been my custodial parent, my protector, but at that point, I didn't feel like she protected me from it even back then. She said she didn't know what to say to her brother and didn't want to believe that he would do something like that. (She actually said that.')

But even at that time, when those memories and those feelings resonated, she never said anything. We revisited this in my twenties and my forties, and we had a conversation before she was killed because my uncle was sick, and my mom wanted to see him. She kept beating around the bush around me, saying things like, "I need to go see my brother."

I told her, "Mom, that's your brother. You can go see him if you want to. You don't have to feel bad about telling me you want to see your brother because he's been hospitalized. My issue is with him and what he did to me. I'm not trying to make it your issue."

I felt like she made it clear when I was eighteen that she did not know how to approach him; again, she did not protect me. Then, in my 20s, she was uncomfortable with that conversation and kept it under the rug. So, I left that alone; I didn't hold that against her that she still wanted a relationship with her brother. He's still alive, and I don't have a relationship with him, and I'm okay with that.

I've Been Through the Storm

When I was eleven, we moved to Manning, SC, more than 150 miles from Benson, NC, and about 200 miles from Lexington. I wasn't that happy to leave all my friends in Benson, but I was glad to get away from Momma's brother. I hoped I'd never see him again! My first memory in South Carolina was Hurricane Hugo. This dangerous Category 5 hurricane hit the South Carolina coast in September 1989. It caused horrific damage in the millions and immeasurable loss of life in the southeastern United States and the northeastern Caribbean. I had never been in a major storm like that before. We lived in a shotgun house, meaning you could see straight from the front door to the back door to the end and all the rooms' doorways.

We were so terrified during that storm in our house. The ceiling caved in all the way, starting in one part of the house, and going to another. We moved from one room to another, and the roof would cave in each time. It was as if it was following us; we were terrified. We were in the kitchen, trembling under a mattress, when it was finally over. We didn't think we would survive Hurricane Hugo, but we did. For years afterward, we teased each other about who was most afraid during the storm. I can laugh about it now, but I surely didn't laugh then.

High School Sweethearts

I met Marvin, my future husband, at McDonald's in Manning, SC.
It was 1990, and I was in transition to high school. My cousins
and I had gone to a football jamboree, where multiple high
school football teams came to compete in simulated games to
prepare their student-athletes. We lived in the rural area of
Manning as if Manning was not country enough. My brother
Dwayne worked at McDonald's. He sometimes worked a four-
hour shift that allowed my cousins and me to socialize outside of
school and at home. We would often go up to McDonalds to hang
out while he worked his shift.

Being at home in the country was boring. There was absolutely
nothing to do. Today's kids would not know what to do without
cable TV, video games, or mobile phones. Our solution to our
boredom was to hang out at my brother's job. My cousins, some
friends and I went to McDonald's after the football jamboree.
Marvin and his friends were sitting in McDonald's. Again, a
chance encounter with **the man who would become my
husband and life partner.**

When we passed Marvin's table, I heard a "pssst pssst" sound, so I turned around and saw this group of guys. They were all looking around as if nobody made that sound. Nobody was being flirtatious. So, I turned around and kept walking with my people. Then, I heard the pssst sound again, but we continued to where we decided to sit.

After a while, this dude came to the back of the lobby, where we sat and spoke. He introduced himself, saying his name was Marvin. We started getting familiar, and he discovered I was Charles and Dwayne's little sister. I'm glad that didn't scare him away. He was three years my senior and the same age as Dwayne, but I did not know him from high school.

About two weeks after our encounter, I started ninth grade. When I got off the bus one morning, I went over to be with my friends under the bus port and pointed him out, "That's the dude I met at McDonalds!" That's how it began, from that first time he was flirting with me at McDonald's and speaking with each other to now, 33 years later. We have been married for 25 years with three kids and two grandkids. It still seems like yesterday. How time flies!

Humble Beginnings

I don't remember any time when I was hungry, unclothed, or unsheltered, but I do remember wanting things other kids had, and Mom's answer was always, *"I ain't got no money for that!"* It seems like there was no money for any "extras." I knew we used food stamps for groceries and received government assistance from the food pantry, but momma made that stuff look regular. I didn't realize times were so hard until I was older.

I didn't attend school events, and my wardrobe was quite basic. I didn't wear the latest fashions and name-brand sneakers until high school. But my brothers at Dad's house seemed to have a lot of stuff, which caused some animosities. It was like, how come they live so good at their house, and we are so poor?

In hindsight, I decided in my childhood that I wanted more for my life. I was determined to work hard so my children would never experience the No's I heard most of the time.

My first job was at the Waffle House in 1992. I started working because I needed my own money with a sense of financial independence. I needed the cash because every time I asked for something, Mom didn't have it. My dad only paid $150 for child support, and I had to damn near beg for anything extra! We had just enough to cover the bills. As I said before, sometimes we had a running car, and sometimes we didn't, so I needed my own cash flow.

Every time I asked for something, wanted to do something, or wanted to go somewhere, or something like that, Mom didn't have it. I decided: *I gotta get me a job because I can't take this!*

I was sixteen and started working as a server at Waffle House. I started out waiting tables on the weekends. In my senior year, I had an early release, and I got out of school at 1:00 or 1:30. This meant I could work the second shift. But the second shift meant I didn't make much money because it was dead, so making $2.13 an hour with few tips kept me in poverty. At that time, Waffle House's second shift, at least back when I was there, was the stocking shift. I would prepare the grits and the waffle batter and fill all the condiment bottles. I wanted to learn how to plate and cook food.

Back then, I did not know what I wanted to do with my life, and I did not have culinary career goals; I just wanted to make more money, and cooking the food was the way to accomplish that because regular cooks made $5.50 an hour and master grill operators made twice that amount.

This was an excellent place to start working for someone who just wanted to make some extra money as a waitress, but a great place to start if you have any culinary aspirations to achieve. I was a responsible employee, worked hard, and learned a lot. That experience would take me farther than I ever imagined in culinary arts. It was a challenging first job experience at the age of sixteen.

Looking back, my job was more advanced than if I had just taken my first job as a cashier. My work was much more involved than what you learn as a cashier at any other restaurant.

Throughout high school, I participated in sports every year and every season of the school year. I was a member of the Color Guard all four years. Color Guard was part of the school's marching band, "the flag girls," we were often called. During basketball season, I was a cheerleader; I was a varsity cheerleader all four years.

After cheering during basketball season, I ran track and played softball in the same season. We had practices and games on alternative days. The games were on different days because the fields were so close to each other. I would have track practice and then softball practice or vice versa.

Sadly, my mom did not see me in action at any of the practices, games, or meets. It caused a bit of strain on our mother-daughter bond. I thought she would never see me cheer or play a sport. With sports, I was very competitive and good at whatever I did. Winning fueled my motivation which also added to my confidence. I felt a bit annoyed and neglected that she didn't come to not one game! Between her working and only making time for the married man she was in love with, it was never a priority to see me in my sports. Though I did participate in the Homecoming court and other pageants, and she came to see me once, I didn't win. I didn't expect to win with a hand-me-down dress and old shoes that didn't even match the dress. They were just black, and momma said, "Black matches everything," and I had to do my hair and makeup. I didn't even place.

My most memorable time in high school was my ninth-grade year. Crushing on Marvin was the highlight of my day. I would wait for him to peek in on me in my 7th-period Spanish class after he returned from vocational school. Vocational students were not even supposed to be in the building because they were finished for the day, but he would sneak in, stand at the door, wink his eye, and blow kisses at me. As you can imagine, that would take my attention away from the lesson, and my grins and giggles would direct Mr. Cribb to go to the door and see why I was distracted. I'm reminiscing with a big smile y'all!

After Marvin graduated in 1991, I just wanted to finish high school. 1994 couldn't come fast enough. I didn't have any favorite subjects or teachers. I was just an average student. I had a C average and didn't want to attend college. I just wanted to be done with school. I didn't have anyone I saw as a role model other than The Huxtables from the Cosby Show, and of course, that was a different world.

I found out I was pregnant. This was just two weeks before I graduated high school. Throughout the summer, I quickly decided that I was going to move forward with my college education. I was determined to go to college; I wanted more for my life. I tried to avoid getting stuck in a small town. I had learned that Columbia Junior College would be a good fit for me because I could get an apartment and they had a business program. I enrolled at Columbia Junior College in August 1994 and was about four months pregnant. I completed the first semester, but when we got out on Christmas break to return to school, I gave birth to Darius on January 2, 1995.

(*"Not to confuse you, but yes, I named my first son Darius after my brother Darius. I didn't know my brother, but I grew fond of the bond I thought we would've had from the stories momma told me about him."*)

When it was time to return to school after the break, I didn't return because my doctor wouldn't release me for another three months. Although I had to sit out for a quarter, I was determined to go back to school because I decided I didn't want to be that statistic of being a person who got stuck. I didn't want to be the person who had a baby out of wedlock, right out of school and never finished her education, and never did anything significant with her life. Again, I had this determination inside of me.

I had developed the attitude of: "**I must finish what I start.**"

I didn't want my story to be, "Well, she didn't finish school because she had a baby."

I wanted to avoid my opportunity to do something or not do something because of a lack of resources, lack of education, lack of determination, lack of encouragement, or lack of courage.

I had grown up unable to go on the same trips as my peers, wear the latest fashions, or do something special. We had very little money, and I didn't have any of the privileges I saw others have.

This made me a determined young woman to create opportunities. I didn't want to be limited by my past or loaded with excuses, "I can't because I have a son." I wanted to be able to do what I wanted to do. I decided to be better than the examples before me.

I graduated in 1996 from Columbia Junior College in Columbia, South Carolina, with an Associate's Business Administration degree. Marvin and I got married that next fall, October 11, 1997. Our second son, Jayvon, was born in November 1998. I also completed the Cosmetology program at Kenneth Shuler's School of Cosmetology that year.

MY FIRST HUSTLE

I was very determined, even when I was younger. Creating opportunities and making things happen has been vital to me for the longest time. We entered my oldest son in a lot of modeling competitions when he was a toddler. It started when my Mother-in-law would enter him in baby contests for church fundraisers. Darius would win trophies for raising the most money in these contests. He was a very handsome kid, and I wanted to show him off on a larger scale. I was aiming for commercials and TV because he was brilliant. He was talking at 11 months. I entered him into a contest at JCPenney's. With this competition, I had to submit his headshots and portfolio.

We didn't have camera phones in 1998. I didn't have professional headshots, and they didn't accept studio pictures like those you would take at K-mart or Sears, and since I did not have money for that, I had to raise the money. So, I came up with the idea of doing a fundraiser.

One Saturday, I decided to raise funds by selling hotdogs, slices of cake, and juices on the side of the road near the neighborhood where I lived. I did this to raise enough money to get the pictures made. I only charged $1, $2, and $3 for items, but I met my goal before I knew it. It was much easier than I thought.

At that time, no one knew me, and I had no inclination that I would make a career out of cooking years later. As a young wife, I would cook a little for my family and the restaurants I worked at, but it was different from the type of cooking where I was selling food.

We sold out. I got there at 10 am to set it up and started selling at 11 am. I thought I would be there till 4:00 or 5:00 in the afternoon, but we sold out of food by 2 pm. We sold out of hotdogs. But I still had chili.

At about the time we were closing, a lady stopped by. She wanted some chili dogs. I told her, "We were out of the hot dogs but still have some chili." She said she wanted the chili even without the hot dog and told me it was the best-tasting chili she had ever had. She said that if I opened a restaurant, she would always send people to me. This lady proceeded to order six chili hot dogs, without the hot dog, just the chili and the bun. That's how much she thought of my chili. She bestowed all this love on me with her great reviews of my chili and told me that she knew she would see me again. Wow, so much enthusiasm for me, and it made me feel so good. This came when I needed to see myself as a professional cook or owning a storefront.

Many years later, when I had a storefront location, she entered the store, but I did not recognize her. She gave me an excellent order, and I got it all packaged up for her. She said, "You don't remember who I am, do you?"

I said, "No, ma'am. I see many people coming in and going out of the store." So, she reminded me of her buying chili dogs from me with no dogs many years before. That was an incredible connection for me and one I will never forget.

Becoming The Cake Lady

In 2003, I opened my first storefront bakery. It was a significant accomplishment for me. I still remember the address; it was 1234 St. Andrews Rd., in Columbia, South Carolina. Shortly after opening the storefront, I got so busy that I had to resign from McDonald's because I was beginning to make cakes full-time.

After being in business for a year and a half, I became pregnant with Za'Nyah. With my pregnancy complications and the impending birth of my daughter Za'Nyah in 2005, I was forced to close the location at the very end of December 2004. But in 2007, I was ready to resume the brick-and-mortar business, so we opened our next location on Hard Scrabble Rd. I stayed there for the next six years.

While owning and operating my bakery, from 2008 to 2010, I worked as the Head Chef at Chi Psi Fraternity House at the University of South Carolina. I needed a regular paycheck while I was building my clientele. I used that income to pay for marketing and advertising of The Cake Lady. I was pursuing my bachelor's degree from 2005-2009. 2009 I graduated from South University (Columbia, South Carolina) with a Bachelor of Arts in Business Administration. Between 2009 and 2012, I expanded to three storefront locations. I also had a venue, Midtown Celebrations, where I planned, catered, and hosted special events.

Fact check: *By the time I was 25, I was a wife to my high school sweetheart and a mother of two sons; I had an associate degree and a cosmetology license and had taught myself how to bake and decorate cakes good enough to open a bakery. In the next five years, I would have added a princess to The Hilton 5 family, earned a bachelor's degree in business administration, head chef at a fraternity house at USC, operated a total of three bakery locations and an events venue, hosting and catering at star-studded events, while growing into a local celebrity myself. Everywhere I went, people knew me or of me. I felt like I was on top of the world! Then I learned the hard lesson that all good things do come to an end.*

ANEW

In 2013, I moved to Atlanta, GA to rebuild and rebrand. Marvin had been living and working here since 2011. He traveled home to Columbia, SC every weekend until we finally moved. Immediately, I hit the ground running, building my network. In 2015, I opened a restaurant near the Mercedes Benz Stadium in the Castleberry Hill neighborhood called In The Kut. It was short-lived, but what an experience it was!

Come 2016; I was given the opportunity to be a contestant on Food Network's Cake Wars. I competed against other bakers for a chance to win $10,000. Although I did not win, being nationally recognized and competing on such a prestigious platform felt great. It felt like a validation of me as a professional cake artist.

In 2017 I received another exciting phone call from producers. This time it is from a show on Netflix called Sugar Rush. I was genuinely feeling blessed to get the chance to live out my dreams as a celebrity chef on TV. I thought God was telling me, "It's only up from here, Mo!" I just knew it was time for my elevation. But just as fast as I got my fingertips on what felt like a success, I lost grip on that when my health took a traumatic turn.

GET THE HELL OUT THE KITCHEN

About a year after I competed on Netflix's "Sugar Rush," the producers of the television show "Hell's Kitchen" gave me a call inviting me to an audition to compete on their show. This was a big deal. It wasn't "Chopped," but as you may know, Hell's Kitchen was a reality cooking show that premiered on Fox in 2005. Celebrity chef Gordon Ramsay hosted the series. More recently, the show was rebranded and is now called "Battle of the Ages."

This was so exciting.

I was a self-taught chef that never studied at a fancy culinary arts school. I competed twice on national television. I couldn't afford the tuition to get a culinary arts degree. But here I was, getting ready to compete. Pretty darn good for me.

During the audition week, I planned the menu for the food I would use. I drove to the audition with my food and was eventually called upon to show what I could do. It was a long day that started with such great excitement. It was time to present my dish, my famous Pineapple rice bowl. A pineapple, halved and gutted, filled with fried rice, diced pineapples, fresh veggies topped with shrimp, and lobster, drizzled with teriyaki sauce.

Sounds delicious, right? Well, it slid a bit, and I almost lost the whole thing! I needed one of the dishes for a presentation. I needed to serve what was in the bowl so that the judges could taste it. I had difficulty getting the dish out of the bag and setting it up.

Then it was time to be judged, which did not go well. They had seen me fumble with my hands and could see my enlarged knuckles, which were very noticeable. They wanted to know what was going on with my hands. They were very nice about it, but asking was their job.

They wondered if I would be able to cut and chop food with my hands. Would I be able to use utensils? Could I stand for long periods of time? They asked if I would be able to lift fifty pounds. The answer to all those questions was no. That wonderful day ended terribly, and my drive home was long and sad.

MY WORLD IS CRASHING

It kept sinking in that I could not go on another show. Where was my dream going? My situation had gotten worse. I was having a lot of physical difficulties. Just handling the utensils was a problem. My faithful hands were failing me, which allowed me to do great things in the kitchen with food and intricate cake designs.

I stopped recording my "Cooking Live with Chef Mo" show. My self-confidence was shot. It kept sinking in more and more. I was feeling crushed about my situation. I was turning down cooking and baking gigs. I was not able to make a delivery without assistance. I couldn't do anything by myself with food preparation and cooking anymore.

I have worked two or three jobs ever since as a teenager. I always thrived on being able to bring home some bacon myself. I had taught my boys and daughter that I contributed financially to the household. I was teaching my daughter about making money and not worrying about somebody having to take care of her. But it's always a bonus to have a partner.

Marvin was great. He didn't push me to work. "Do what's needed to get you back healthy. Whatever we need, I'll take care of that." When we had first heard that I was diagnosed with a disease called Scleroderma and there was no cure, he said, "We'll pray that God heals your body. That's what we are going to do."

SCLERODERMA

I was first diagnosed with Scleroderma in 2017. One reason for writing this book is to increase awareness of what it is, how physically debilitating it can be, and how it impacted my life.

Something Like a Doctor

Scleroderma is an autoimmune, rheumatic, and chronic disease that affects the body by hardening connective tissues.

"Connective tissues" add strength to organs and other parts of the body. This tissue is made of proteins such as collagen in the skin. Scleroderma literally means hard skin.

With Scleroderma, a person's immune system works against itself, making collagen as if an injury needs repairing. The cells do not turn off as they should and make too much collagen. The extra collagen in the tissues can prevent the body's organs from functioning normally. The immune system protects the body by fighting off foreign invaders such as viruses and infections.

The severity of scleroderma varies from person to person. It can be a mild annoyance, cause significant clinical problems, or become life-threatening and life changing. Some people have episodes where the illness improves or even goes into remission, but I haven't been that lucky yet.

"An Illness That Does Not Go Away seem pretty unfair, right?"

Scleroderma is a chronic and rare disease that lasts for a lifetime, and there is no cure, but there are treatments that can effectively prevent or limit the damage caused by this chronic disease.

No one knows why or how it develops, but my doctor suggested that my gastric sleeve surgery could have triggered Scleroderma's debut. Some experts report that six out of seven patients are women.

Scleroderma does not seem to be genetic; it is, however, common for family members to have other autoimmune diseases like thyroid disease, rheumatoid arthritis, or lupus. In fact, my father had Multiple Sclerosis (Ataxia). He passed away in 2014, and one of my mom's older sisters, Aunt Cleo, died from complications of Scleroderma over 40 years ago. According to her daughters, Vera and Barbara Jean, her fingers began to curl noticeably, then her skin turned very dark, and it felt like leather. She developed lung involvement and her mobility severely declined, and in just four years, she lost her battle with this disease. If you are experiencing joint stiffness, muscle pain, fatigue, or acid reflux, I encourage you to look into your family history and also discuss this with your doctor.

African Americans and Native Americans generally have more severe Scleroderma than Caucasians. These findings suggest a hereditary component to Scleroderma and other autoimmune disorders.

Early Symptoms

Before I was diagnosed, I noticed swelling in my fingers and toes and tingling in my hands and feet when I woke up. When I mentioned it to my doctor, she told me it was Carpal Tunnel Syndrome in my hands. That didn't seem too far-fetched at the time because I had been working with my hands for many years, from doing hair to cake decorating.

I was familiar with that name because I was acquainted with many stylists who had experienced it. The more I researched Carpal Tunnel and compared that info to my symptoms, the less I found that I had in common with that condition.

Being Your Own Advocate

I told my doctor, "That's not what's going on with my hands. Perhaps I need a second opinion."

The doctor gave me a referral to a Rheumatologist. The Rheumatologist did a few tests, asked questions, and told me I had Rheumatoid Arthritis.

This condition did match some of what I was experiencing, but the numbing and tingling were unanswered, so I kept asking questions. I didn't stay with this particular Rheumatologist very long because the bedside manner of this practice wasn't too inviting, so I sought another doctor. I saw two more specialists before I found Dr. Tsagaris, a Rheumatologist specializing in Scleroderma at Emory Clinic. Dr. Tsagaris did a series of tests:

- Complete blood count (CBC) – to evaluate red and white blood cells.
- Comprehensive metabolic panel (CMP) – to evaluate organ function and chemical and electrolyte balances.
- Urinalysis
- Thyroid function tests

These are some categories of the series of tests:

- ANA: Antinuclear Antibody Assay
- Nailfold Capillary Test
- Skin Tests: Modified Rodnan Skin Score
- Pulmonary (Lung) Function Tests
- Pulmonary Arterial Hypertension (PAH) Tests

Diagnosis (March 2017): Scleroderma

I was diagnosed with Systemic Sclerosis, aka Scleroderma, in March 2017. By now, my fingers and hands were stiff and puffy more frequently and changed to red, white, or blue regularly.

Raynaud's

Cold temperatures, anxiety, or stress usually trigger Raynaud's phenomenon. This happens when my blood vessels go into a temporary spasm that blocks the blood flow, causing my fingers to turn white when I'm too cold, blue, and red as my blood flow returns. This occurs because of excess collagen that has narrowed the blood vessels and an overreaction of the skin.

Raynaud's (pronounced RAY-KNOWDS) phenomenon is a common condition.

A small percentage of people with Raynaud's phenomenon develop Scleroderma. Conversely, almost everyone with Scleroderma has Raynaud's phenomenon. Most people initially experience tight and swollen fingers and will likely have Raynaud's phenomenon, a CREST symptom.

CREST Symptoms

CREST name and symptoms include:

- Calcinosis - deposition of calcified nodules in the skin causing it to thicken and tighten.
- Raynaud's phenomenon - exaggerated vasoconstriction in extremities on exposure to cold.
- Esophageal dysmotility - atrophy of gut wall muscles resulting in dysphagia.
- Sclerodactyly - thickening of the skin of the fingers, distal to the metacarpophalangeal joints.
- Telangiectasia - dilation of capillaries in the face, palms, and mucous membranes.

Complications result when the CREST symptoms progress. As you see, I had a number of these symptoms (marked by *):

- Ulcers on fingers and toes*
- Lung damage
- Heart problems
- Kidney problems
- *Dental problems
- *Dry eyes and mouth
- Gastrointestinal Problems*

Currently, there's no cure for Scleroderma, so doctors will find the best treatments to decrease the severity of the specific symptoms and manage or prevent additional complications.

I became really depressed when I was described as a palliative care patient.

Do you know what that means? Palliative Care is specialized medical care for people with serious illnesses like cancer, heart failure, etc. In layman's terms, patients in palliative care receive medical care for their symptoms to make them comfortable, but there is not always a cure.

To hear there is no cure for Scleroderma is frightening. I instinctively thought the worst. When my doctor gave me the news, she said, "Every person is different; I encourage you to research symptoms and treatments." Then she emphasized, "PLEASE DON'T FOCUS ON THE IMAGES ON THE INTERNET BECAUSE EVERY CASE IS DIFFERENT!"

After telling me how disturbing and intimidating the images would look to anyone learning about Scleroderma for the first time, what do you think I did? I typed in SCLERODERMA and clicked on images, and I lost it!

I cried for days, maybe even weeks. I panicked! I woke up every morning and rushed to the mirror to see if my face had changed while I slept. Three years after my initial diagnosis, I began to experience some of the physical changes I feared.

Treating Scleroderma

Treatment typically focuses on inflammation, autoimmunity, vascular issues, and tissue fibrosis (the thickening and scarring of the connective tissue surrounding the internal organs).

In the beginning, the pain was indescribable.

It's been a struggle and many trials trying to customize the best treatment for me. My doctor prescribed many medications, and the side effects added to the many symptoms I was already experiencing. I was getting pain relief through nonsteroidal, anti-inflammatory drugs, opioids, and corticosteroids until I whipped up a batch of cannabutter. I prefer consuming cannabis or CBD for my pain because it's relaxing and helps me rest comfortably.

Itching is a side effect of some medications and a result of having extremely tight and dry skin due to my skin stretching so much, allowing minimal moisture absorption. I have spent a lot of time and money trying to find the best products to ease my itchy skin with lotions, body butters, and moisturizers, and for this, I've discovered that CBD salves are my favorite go-to. It soothes the itching and calms the inflammation at the same time.

I take the highest medication dosage to slow down the progression of skin thickening and minimize damage to my internal organs. These medications suppress the immune system. Eating a clean and organic diet has proven to be the best recipe for strengthening my immune system, reducing the inflammation that causes most of the pain, and improving my gut health which helps decrease GERD and constipation. Of course, drinking plenty of water and getting proper rest helps reduce fatigue. These changes proved essential for managing my digestive tract function to optimize nutritional intake because my appetite is still minimal.

I have regained some muscle strength through physical therapy and exercise, but my physical abilities are still limited. My muscle strength disappeared like magic, or so it seemed, and it's been hard trying to rebuild my memory.

Blood Transfusion

Currently, I have regular appointments every three months to see the rheumatologist because of the medication that I'm on. They do bloodwork to ensure I have no kidney issues because the medication is so strong that it could cause renal failure.

At one of my standard appointments in 2018, my friend Bonita, who lives in Columbia, South Carolina, accompanied me. She is a physical therapist knowledgeable about medical terminology and medications. She is also very good at looking up the side effects of those medications. When I began taking all these medications, she asked me about the side effects and what would happen if I took this med with that one. I was not able to answer her. That's what motivated her to drive from her home to Atlanta. She wanted to be there to help me fully comprehend the medications' effects. She went to the doctor with me, and she asked several questions. She knew about the impact of my condition, and she was aware that I was losing mobility and suggested that I should be in occupational and physical therapy. Based on her work as a physical therapist, she was very knowledgeable about joints and muscles and how the body can work against itself.

After we left the appointment, the doctor called me within three hours, and she said my hemoglobin was 5.4 and explained that a healthy hemoglobin range is 11 to 13. The doctor wanted me to go to the nearest hospital immediately. I was told that I was in a stroke zone.

I went to the hospital. I ended up having to get a blood transfusion. I stayed in the hospital for the next four days. I was pretty scared. Other than childbirth, I've never been hospitalized and have never had all that attention coming my way. I entered an ER full of people. They took my blood pressure. They rolled me straight to the back with no waiting.

I didn't know it was that serious. I was scared from the time I entered the hospital until I was discharged. It took two days to get the blood I needed to get my hemoglobin up enough to discuss discharging. But after that, they wanted me to drink this solution to move my bowels before I left the hospital because they wanted to test my bowels and perform an endoscopy and colonoscopy.

A gallon was a lot of solution to drink and impossible for me to complete because I had the gastric sleeve. I told the nurse, "I'm not going to be able to drink all of that." But she was firm and insisted that I needed to try.

I began to take small sips.

Since the blood transfusion was completed, they wanted to transfer me to another room while I waited for a bowel movement. This goes on for hours and hours and overnight and until the next morning. This is another day in the hospital. I am a foodie, so I am growing mad because they do not allow me to eat any food. I am just drinking this solution all day long. Eventually, I had a bowel movement, even though I did not drink the entire solution content.

So, I thought I was done and ready for discharge. But that did not happen. I was wondering why I had not seen the doctor. It's Friday, and I went into the hospital on Monday. I was ready to get out of there. I waited on the doctor to make her rounds, but she never came. I became very frustrated. It is now dinner time. I'm still in the hospital. I'm ready to go home. "Why am I still here?" I did not want to be there for the weekend. I didn't want to be charged for just sitting there occupying space. They had already taken the IV out, so I was not getting any more medication. Now it was eight o'clock; I was very aggravated sitting in that hospital room.

I asked for the head nurse and the attending doctor. They never came. Then the head nurse came in, and I told her I wanted to go home, "I don't understand why I am still here. The blood transfusion finished two days ago, and I'm no longer receiving an IV. I'm not getting any more medication." The cost doesn't stop ticking as long as I am in that hospital bed. I had to get out of there.

The head nurse told me I must sign voluntary discharge papers to be discharged. So that happened, and after two more hours, I got released. In situations like this, you have to be your advocate when you are in the hospital or at your doctor's appointments. It was enriching and empowering because I was able to fight for myself.

The Mo Experience

As I said, I was diagnosed in 2017 but didn't begin to see rapid changes until 2019 through 2020. My fingers curled so badly I could no longer wash my body with my dominant hand; I still couldn't! I had to cut my hair short because I couldn't comb or style my hair anymore, not to mention it was falling out in patches anyway because of all the medications. My mobility declined rapidly.

At the start of the 2018-2019 school year, I was the head Chef at Charles R. Drew High School in Clayton County, Georgia, outside Atlanta. Things started out great, but by the end of the spring semester of 2019, I could barely walk to my classroom, much less teach students how to spread butter on toast.

After that school year, I hung up my apron and bitterly passed my Chef duties to my daughter, Za'Nyah. It was bitter-sweet because she took over because I wanted her to, not because she wanted to. Although we can wear the same shoes, my footprints were a big act to follow for her at the age of thirteen. Please understand, Za'Nyah is well-trained and extremely talented in the kitchen. I taught her everything I knew, and she is a terrific learner. Sadly, I had to accept that cooking was my passion, not hers; I didn't want to quit.

INTERIM CHEF

A friend of mine from high school is the Principal at Charles R. Drew High School in Riverdale, Georgia. She posted on Facebook that her school was looking to hire math and culinary teachers. I contacted her and asked what the requirements were for the Chef position. She told me that the applicant had to have a degree in culinary arts and a teaching certification. I didn't have either, but I possess a bachelor's degree in business administration, and I've been a Chef and entrepreneur for over 20 years. I hoped my experience would have been equivalent to the degree, but unfortunately, that wasn't the case. I ended up getting hired as a substitute teacher.

I agreed to take the position. My husband, my kids, and the people around me were in disbelief! They were like, "What? Girl, you don't even like kids like that!"

When I first started, I felt like I was in the movie "Lean on Me," starring Morgan Freeman. The class was chaotic, and they had no structure. I knew I had to go into the first class with a strong presence because I remembered how students would take advantage of the substitutes in high school. I was determined to let them know I was in charge.

We did our introductions. After a while, the students settled down. I introduced myself and told them I had been on national television food shows and been through competitions. Because of the non-disclosure agreements I had signed with the food shows, I couldn't go into details. Some respect was built for me because I told them about my experience with cooking. They began to listen. It was an exciting year.

I found out there needed to be books and food to use. I needed more to start with. I had no teaching experience, and I needed a culinary degree. I did have self-confidence, though, and knew I could teach anything in my mind, so I improvised. I treated the classes like businesses.

I told the students from the start that I would refer to the classes as businesses because I have been a business owner for so long. Everything I do is about operating a food business serving customers. Because I was treating it like a business, I wanted the students to wear the standard Chef uniforms that the curriculum requires. They were given a deadline for ordering their uniforms; after that deadline, the participation grades would begin. I distributed uniforms to every student. Each student had a class fee of $25. I sent letters out to the parents to attend a class conference so I could introduce myself to the parents and inform them of my school plans for their students.

Most were impressed that I planned to teach culinary like a business. With any business, when you go to work, you must wear a uniform. I expected that the students would wear their uniforms to all our classes. I made no exceptions. If the student did not wear a uniform, they got a zero for their class participation. That's when the meeting grew a little tense. I began to lose a few parents' support of the zero grade, but I stuck with it because what are we preparing them for if they are not learning rules and consequences?

There was also some uproar when I communicated my expectations about the class fee. I explained that the food in the storage was expired and that I needed food for the kitchen to begin to teach their students anything. I further explained that the class fees were the same as if they needed to purchase a textbook or other supplies.

I wanted to collect the class fees to buy food in bulk which would stretch the money. I explained that we would use the food we would start with to make food that we could sell and make more money to buy more food and repeat the process. But we needed some "starter" money.

It was a tedious step for starters because it was a Title 1 school, meaning the area had high numbers or percentages of children in poverty, so some families couldn't afford the $25 plus the uniform fee.

The principal allowed me to move forward with the class fees because it was necessary to get the burners lit and start cooking. There were a few unhappy parents, but eventually, they softened up because their students fell in love with "The Mo Experience."

I was pleased with the classroom. I remember how my eyes lit up when I went there for the first time. It was a special place with stoves, state-of-the-art equipment, tools, and most importantly, passion. It was mine to use. I had a similar kitchen as the Chi Psi fraternity House Chef at the University of South Carolina.

Some students had a genuine reason for their difficulty with the class fees. I remember one student who told me she could not get her uniform. She said, "Chef Mo, I can't get my uniform because I barely have a place to live. I stay with my aunt, and she tries to do a lot for me, but I'm pretty much on my own."

Another student with the same difficulty getting a uniform told me that her mom works two jobs and can't afford $25. These sounded reasonable to motivate me to do what I could to help them.

Some of the kids could help with the food inventory, but for the ones that needed assistance, I went to social media. I did a couple of videos aimed at raising money for the students. I explained to the program that we needed food for the sixty students and how I wanted to prepare the students to be chefs. I told my followers that we needed their help, and they HELPED! "Do you have anything extra you can contribute?" I asked.

Thankfully, people started to send in donations. Some used the Cash app, and others dropped off food, plates, beverages, and napkins at the school or designated pick-up locations.

Ultimately, 188 students (for all the classes) paid the $25 class fee, and some paid $50 to pay it forward for someone else. People were generous and wanted this program to start and be successful.

I began by purchasing food that you had to cut and chop so that I could teach those skills and how to be safe in the kitchen. I ordered textbooks from ServSafe, a company that provides workforce training in the restaurant industry. I used their textbooks during class time and to help guide the program.

At the end of the school year, the seniors took the certification exam because they had been in the program for three years.

I would go to Sam's Club to buy chips, water, sodas, juices, candy, and other things to sell to students after school. These after-class sales raised money for us, but they did something else. The students began learning money management, customer service, profit and loss, and other business skills.

My teaching style was to make the class as hands-on as possible. When you learn cash handling, you also learn customer service. I used the experience to teach profit and loss and inventory control and management. That whole experience created a lot of teachable moments for the students to help them be successful. I was always linking what we were learning at school to success in business. We completed many get-started activities and learning and eventually went into the kitchen to cook. Some students genuinely wanted to learn, while others did not want to cook.

I made it clear from the beginning that I had little patience for unsafe kitchen practices. I pushed safety all the time.

Kids who did not want to cook could sit at their desks and study; as long as they had on their uniforms, they earned their participation grades.

My most memorable time as the Interim Chef was watching all my classes/businesses complete a Capstone learning project.

One of the projects was a business named the AM PM CAFÉ. It had a bit of a twist. The students sold breakfast items in the afternoon and dinner items in the morning.

For the café, the students created a name for their business, business cards, and an Instagram page. They developed a business plan, budget, menu, and the décor for the grand opening. They set a date for execution when it would be open for the school. I was pleased, and so were the principal, the teachers, the parents, and even some local supporters. The students loved their capstone learning experience. It was fun and challenging, and highly educational. I took pride in it for the kids and myself.

Many of the students took it very seriously and applied themselves. I felt very proud about that because it was like they had their own grand openings. They liked the red carpet and ribbons, confetti, and balloons. It was charming, and the students dove in. I would not be surprised if at least two chefs or restaurant owners came out of that experience.

I loved the Capstone experience, but it was hard on my body. It was a grueling two weeks for my body because I oversaw all of it for seven classes. The work experience consumed me, and it took a lot of effort to get through it.

That's when I started experiencing the pain from being on my feet too long. I was going from across the hall to another part of the school, from class to class, and walking around. The pain got so intense that I began scooting around in my desk chair with wheels on it.

When I was walking, it felt like my hip bones were rubbing bone on bone. When I look back at that time, I think that's when I started experiencing rapid changes in my body.

Right after the Capstone Projects, the school closed for the Christmas holiday. Honestly, I was ready for this break. I thought that I was just tired. For the previous two weeks, I had been swamped and doing much walking and standing. But the pain continued to get worse, and that slowed me down.

When we went back to school, I was never the same. My endurance in the kitchen declined significantly. To compensate in the classroom, I began using my hands less and allowed my assistant to demonstrate in the kitchen while I explained.

Holding utensils was so painful. It reached a point where I could not do much at all because the fatigue was bossing me around. I couldn't move like I was before. All of this was happening right before my eyes. This disease was robbing me of my self-confidence. I felt like I started this big-time "Celebrity Chef," and now all I could do was sit down and talk.

For the rest of the year, I started inviting chefs that had commented on my Facebook page while raising money for the students at the beginning of the school year. They told me they loved what I was doing and said to contact them if I needed help. Well, I NEEDED THEIR HELP!

I promised the school district I would finish the rest of the year, so I asked for that help. I had guest Chefs come into the classes and help me demonstrate food and kitchen techniques. I knew I could not return and teach the following year, so I wanted to finish strong. I was sad about not being able to come back because I had grown to enjoy the students and teaching.

The principal was impressed with what I was teaching and my teaching methods. The parents were impressed by the interest the students showed. They were trying to figure out how to offer me a position with a bachelor's degree in business. But the district would have wanted me to get another certification for cooking and teaching. I didn't want to go back to school, but in the end, it did not matter because I knew I would not be able to return due to the changes in my health.

This may Explain the Fatigue!

I had a blood transfusion during my year at Drew High School. The goal then was to raise my hemoglobin rate and help with fatigue. I was admitted to the hospital to have a blood transfusion. My blood pressure was still low when I left the hospital, but I could be discharged. I was out of work for a week. After the blood transfusion, I was able to go back to work. I felt rested enough to go back to teaching.

I was still experiencing fatigue, swelling, and tight skin during this time. My movement was beginning to be a little slower than usual, but I hadn't yet begun to experience the curling of my fingers.

Falling into a "Funk"

Scleroderma impacted many essential aspects of my life. Although I'm blessed to have a dependable team of family and friends to help manage challenges, my confidence and courage had taken a hit. Scleroderma changed my appearance. It caused my physical abilities to decline significantly. It had made it difficult to do everyday tasks.

During this period of my life, my confidence was crushed. I was always sad. I stopped wanting to eat because I had to have my food cut up and pick it up like a baby. Imagine my frustration. I did try, though. I began to try to pick up a fork. That wasn't easy. I tried to use the fork to put the food into my mouth. That was even more difficult because my forearm was so tight, and the fold in my arm was so tight I could barely put the fork to my mouth.

I couldn't lift things off the floor, put on my socks and shoes, open bottles, or button shirts; I'll tell you, so many things we do daily are taken for granted!

Scleroderma had caused stress, and I worried more than usual. This was ironic because stress and worry impact the severity of the disease. I was in a funk and felt hopeless, but I didn't want help.

I Shifted Priorities and Began to Rebuild My Life.

My quality of life depended on me shifting my priorities. I decided to focus on learning techniques for coping with this condition instead of dwelling on things I could not change.

For example, instead of asking someone to put my socks on, I taught myself how to use my toes to put my socks on. I would lay the footie on the floor, pin one corner of the sock to the floor with my toes and stretch and wiggle the other foot in until I got my toes in the sock. Doing this on the carpet is best so the texture helps you secure the sock. Try it!

I asked God to bring me out of my funk and to be hopeful. I allowed people to help me. I changed my perspective through prayer, meditation, mental, physical, occupational therapy, advocacy, and transparency. Once I got out of that funk and rebuilt my courage and confidence, I began to live out loud again.

I've heard all my life that faith without work is dead. I decided I didn't want to stay in my situation of "I can't do this" and "I can't do that." I decided to push my limits.

I began to create content on social media again, talking about what Scleroderma is and how it has affected me. I host fundraisers to spread awareness about Scleroderma and have donated since 2019 to **www.scleroderma.org**. I've even founded my own non-profit organization called <u>The Mo Experience Foundation, Inc</u>. **www.TheMoExperience.org**. I started a nonprofit to fund scholarships to help aspiring chefs start with a culinary degree/career and spread awareness about Scleroderma.

Trials

My doctors have mentioned IVIG (Intravenous Immunoglobulin) Infusions and Stem Cell Transplant, but it is not FDA-approved, so my insurance will not cover these costly procedures.

If you have an immunodeficiency related to certain infections, inflammatory diseases, or an autoimmune disorder, you may have heard about an infusion treatment called intravenous immunoglobulin, or IVIG. This therapy is primarily designed for situations where you may not have enough antibodies. An IVIG may also be used if your condition doesn't respond to immunosuppressive medications.

IVIG therapy infusion aims to help restore a severely weakened immune system. Your doctor may also recommend an IVIG infusion to help reduce inflammation. This therapy can help prevent your immune system from attacking healthy cells in autoimmune diseases.

In Scleroderma, it is hoped that a stem cell transplant might be able to modify or reset the immune response, potentially reducing, or preventing disease progression. It is possible that stem cells could be used to repair damage caused by Scleroderma in tissues.

I have met three people in my support groups who have had stem cell transplants, and they all have improved exceptionally well. I want to try one of these procedures, but my insurance doesn't pay for either.

CRYING MYSELF TO SLEEP

I went through a period when I was crying myself to sleep in secret and screaming in the shower. I did this when nobody was home because I felt horrible about my position.

When I screamed in the shower, I often cried out to God, "Did I do something wrong? Did I offend somebody too much? Do you want me to see how it feels? Why am I going through this ordeal?"

I had been making a living off the art my hands could create, but now I could not do that. I started as a hairstylist and then developed a love for cooking. And then I developed a passion for decorating. I was self-taught.

I've been creating with my hands and living off my skills for over 20 years. And now I could not hold a spatula. I could not use a knife to cut and chop food. I could not stir a pot. I still have difficulty stirring a pot and handling large kitchen utensils. I don't have much grip or mobility in my hands to do any of those things. I couldn't articulate my feelings about this. But I had many tears because I didn't know how to allocate that energy. I felt like God had shown me my name in the lights, and then the lights went out. The show was over. My vision had ended.

I'M SO GLAD HE PRAYED

If you know the "Ole Southern Church," sing the next few lines.

My husband prayed for me,
had me on his mind,
took the time,
and prayed for me,
I'm so glad he prayed,
I'm so glad he prayed,
I'm so glad he prayed for me!

Marvin was brought up in church and was a servant of the church all his life. He was born into a gospel-singing family and started playing drums at the tender age of six.

His calling was not to preach, dance, shout, or sing, although he can hold a nice tune. Marvin's ministry was to be a leader in his own right—the drum. The instrument provides the foundation for the other musicians to follow. The drummer is the anchor of the band. Being the anchor, a drummer must have confidence. Confidence is what makes a good drummer a great drummer.

His greatness, confidence, leadership, strength, and love of God exude into his interactions with everyone he encounters daily. Still, his strength was being put to the test after my diagnosis. My strength was being tested too.

The pain I had begun to feel was vastly different than any I had ever experienced. You see, Systemic Sclerosis, another name for Scleroderma, can cause the tissues around the joints to stiffen, reducing the range of movement of the joints. It can also cause pain, swelling around the affected joints, and muscle weakness. I wasn't just experiencing pain in one area; it bounced all over my body like a ping-pong ball on fire!

My hips, knees, ankles, fingers, shoulders, and even my jaws would get so stiff I could hardly open my mouth! All the joints in my body would become inflamed, and I didn't know what to do to ease the pain. I laid down and silently cried myself to sleep many nights; little did I know, Marvin heard every sniffle, every prayer, and deep sighs I made. I tried to keep quiet in pleads to God for healing, but I often couldn't contain my outburst. That was indeed a test of Marvin's strength and the foundation of our testimony. He felt helpless and didn't know how to help me ease my pain.

I often soaked in hot Epsom salt baths and got frequent massages with alcohol, Bio Freeze, Bengay, and Icy Hot, but all those things only soothed my inflammation for a short period.

Marvin would wake up around 3:30 am to get ready for work when he was a truck driver for US Foods. His routine was like clockwork. He was never in the military, though his dad was. I guess much of his dad's army training rubbed off onto Marvin.

Marvin laid his clothes out at night, showered, shaved, and filled his backpack with all his truck driver's necessities like hand sanitizer, chips, Vienna sausages, a fruit or two, and his water bottle. He was in bed by 9 pm.

There were a few consecutive mornings I woke up to Marvin kissing me on my forehead and gently pulling the covers up on me; I thought, *what is happening here*? I checked for my panties, thinking, *did he have his way with me while I was asleep? What was he doing standing over me? Why were the covers off me? I was puzzled!*

I couldn't stop thinking about that one particular day. I ran all kinds of scenarios in my head. I didn't want to come out and ask what I was thinking, but I was curious. The next night I went to bed with a mission on my mind. I fell asleep with my eyes wide open, not literally, but with every movement or sound I heard; my eyes opened wide! I was determined to uncover my suspicions.

When I heard his alarm go off at 3:30, I was ready to catch him in the act. He rolled over to my side of the bed and hugged me like usual. Then, he put his hand on my butt... It was actually my right hip, but remember, I thought I was going to catch him red-handed with his hands in the "cookie jar." Anyway, he got up, came to my side of the bed, pulled the covers down to my feet, and nudged me enough to roll on my back. I thought, *Gotcha! I knew he was doing something really sneaky and freaky.* I was playing possum because I wanted to know what he was getting ready to do, so I kept my eyes closed. I was thinking, *is he about to get some cookie before he goes to work? He's gonna be drained before lunchtime.*

I remember turning over like I was asleep, trying to keep him from getting to my goods so easily, but he turned me back over on my back. Then there was a brief pause. I heard what sounded like a bottle unscrewing; I thought, *Is this man seriously gonna put some KY jelly or Motion Lotion on me this time of morning?* I heard him place whatever that was in his hand on the nightstand. He knelt beside me, and I felt his hands, then a kiss on my forehead, from my shoulders to my elbows to my fingers, from my hips to my knees to my feet. I opened my eyes to see that he was kneeling with his head down. He continued to caress my body while still kneeling then I began to hear a very faint sound of weeping.

Marvin lifted his head to check the time, then wiped his eyes. He got up, pulled the covers up, tucked me in snuggly, and kissed me on the forehead. He quickly got dressed for work and hurried out of the house.

As soon as I heard the front door close, I sat up in bed and reached over to the nightstand to see what he had placed there. It wasn't KY jelly or Motion Lotion; it was Anointed Healing Oil that we got from our pastor, Sammy C. Smith, founder of Grace Cathedral in Sumter, SC.

I find humor in the fact that I thought my husband was trying to be intimate when it was evident what Marvin was doing. He was covering me in that healing oil and was praying over my body from head to toe!

Please understand I broke out in a Shabach praise at that moment! Crying, and I mean the ugly cry that Viola Davis can make. Praying. Praising God for a husband that took the time and prayed over me.

That was the embodiment of the vows we exchanged before God, our family, and friends Saturday, October 11, 1997, when we promised to love and to cherish, for better or worse, for richer or poorer, in SICKNESS and HEALTH till death do us part according to God's holy law.

He stood firm on his word; he loves me and cherishes my life, our family, and the legacy that we have built together. God knows we have been Better but seen Worse, we've been Richer as well as Poorer, and my Health wasn't always as fragile. Still, the way he rolled up his sleeves, ready to face sickness with me and everything that Scleroderma was throwing my way, showed me God's purpose for placing him in my life and joining us as one 25 years ago.

I'm so glad he prayed for me!

The Foundation

I saw our new home before we broke ground. It was a vision I had of my next venture, a cooking show, and my very own kitchen was the set.

We were fresh in our current home in Fairburn, a suburb of Atlanta. We had only been there for a year. I posted many pictures during the process of building our home. I posted photos of the property after it was cleared off, when they poured the concrete, framed the house, and everything. It was an exciting time for us, and I shared that on Facebook. Whenever Marvin and I went there, I would take pictures and post them.

We would walk the grounds. We prayed on the concrete foundation. When the frame was up, and we could go into the house, we wrote scriptures on different parts of the house. When it was almost done, we did the same thing, writing scriptures and saying prayers. Because of all the posting I was doing; people were following our process. Right from the beginning, I had a vision of our house. I had the vision before the foundation was poured. I knew what every room would look like, how it would be designed, the color, everything.

Once the house was up, we moved everything in. When we moved in, it was the most straightforward setup I had ever done in a home because I had a picture in my mind of how it was to look.

Because we had posted so many pictures, many friends and family wanted to visit and see the house. They wanted to be part of the process. They were proud of us, admiring Marvin and me for what we were doing with our lives.

I asked them to call in advance, and many did. Sometimes they stayed for dinner. We enjoy entertaining just as much as I enjoy cooking and baking.

As soon as we finished staging the house like I wanted, I began producing and performing my Facebook Live Show @Cooking Live with Chef Mo. My format was accessible and friendly. I would invite a business owner, entertainer, influencer, or even a motivational speaker to come to our house and talk about their brand or what events or special offers they had coming up. As an entrepreneur myself, I thrived on being able to support another entrepreneur.

I had a large audience and got positive feedback about the show. During the show, my guest would cook with me. We had fun and ate good. My guests were thrilled because they gained followers, got exposure on my show, and had The Mo Experience first-hand. The show was taken away from me when my health changed. It killed everything for a while. It killed my motivation.

Bath & Body Works

Sunday is the day I've designated for bathing, my Bath Day. I was embarrassed to need help doing something so personal. For most people, your bath time is time with yourself. Your naked alone time, whether that is naked in the mirror, naked in your thoughts, or naked in your spirituality. It is personal time that most people often enjoy alone. Having to rely on someone for self-care and hygiene, I felt stripped of my dignity even when I realized I needed help. It has taken me time to adjust to being so dependent on another person, even my husband, with whom I have taken plenty of baths.

My doctor suggested that warm baths should be helpful to my aching muscles, stiff joints, and dimmed spirits. It's also great for relaxation and meditation, so I gave in and welcomed the help. When I say help, I mean the "Orderly" or "Home Nurse" kind of help.

I cannot physically lift my legs high enough to get in our garden tub without help. I also can only sit in the tub if I am lowered into the tub. My knees and hips are so stiff that there is very little range of motion. Getting out is even harder for Marvin. He literally has to lift my dead weight of 140 pounds out of water.

The more I got comfortable with Bath Day, the more intimate we began to make it. I mean intimacy goes far beyond sexual intercourse. He is very nurturing and has a unique way of making me feel better about needing his aid. I still have balance issues in the shower, which can be dangerous. It's better than it was, but I must be careful.

On any given Sunday, I'd hear Marvin call my name from upstairs to come to our bedroom. As I walk up the stairs, rose petals lead to our bedroom. When I enter the room, there are more pedals. My favorite scents from Bath & Body Works are burning, and smooth R&B music is on (usually, Jodeci or Jasmine Sullivan is playing over the radio). The bubbles towered over the tub's rim, covering up any traces of Epsom salt and green rubbing alcohol.

First, he lifts my right leg, slowly places it in the tub, and then lifts my left leg. He then puts the rubber donut in place to lower me onto it. He always ensures the water is not too hot and has an ice-cold glass of water on standby in case I get overheated.

While I'm soaking, I use that time to read, pray, or meditate, and sometimes I do them all. While I'm relaxing, Marvin is getting my towels ready. He usually throws a couple of towels in the dryer, especially in the wintertime. Once I'm done soaking, he comes back in to wash every inch of my body, so fresh and so clean. Shout out to Outkast!

After getting me out of the tub, he dried me off with a hot towel. *Lord, that feels amazing! I was saying to myself.* My tight skin gets dry and uncomfortable very quickly. My muscles might love that hot water, but my skin does not, so I must be moisturized immediately. This is my favorite part! Now I get moisturized, massaged, stretched, and fondled. And did I say MOISTURIZED?

I never knew love like this. He treats me like his queen; he is my hero and king! No doubt about that.

I SWITCHED FROM "WHY ME" TO "WHY NOT ME"?

Over time and with insights from others, I began to see more options for me. Instead of thinking it was over, I noticed I could take a different path. I couldn't decorate cakes anymore, but to my surprise, painting became a new talent. If I could not see my name in lights for cooking or decorating cakes, that doesn't mean I can't see my name in lights for something else.

My friend Pastor Nelson reminded me to know that it is not over. It is just getting started. Remember that God's interpretation of those lights may tell you another story.

I reached a point of transition, to shake it off by taking every day how it comes, rain or shine. I decided to live my life one day at a time.

I remember going to sleep many nights with my prayers, asking God, "Why me? Why did I get this disease? I can't do this, and I can't do that!

I began waking up in the morning and saying, "Why not me?"

I had not been posting pictures on Facebook. I hadn't done a video broadcast of "Cooking Live with Chef Mo" in a while.

I remember getting emails asking if I was okay because I had not posted in a while. People were checking in with me. They were wondering why they had not seen any activity from me. They had a fear of missing out (FOMO) people. They wanted to know, "What's going on with you?"

Over the years, my journey has touched many people. I remember one girl, a young mom, texted me to check on me and shared her story. She said, "I haven't seen you in a while. I just wanted to let you know that I am thinking about you. I went to the doctor about a year ago because of joint pain. I first thought about how you described how you went to the doctor and got tests done. The doctor told me one thing, but it was something else. But I just remembered you saying not to give up and to ask questions and to get a second opinion if you need to. And I did just that. Thank you."

I like hearing testimonials like that.

Today, whenever I am doing a fundraiser or an event, she sends me a donation of $100. Every time. Her testimonial has shown me that my story has helped others keep moving forward.

MY FIRST BOOK

In March 2020, I finished my book, "The Mo Experience: Autobiography and Cookbook." My plan was that people would buy the book and would also buy my seasonings and sauces. My customers could buy a VIP package that was attractive to the eye and would contain the cookbook, a custom apron, and two of my sauces.

I was excited about doing a book tour and serving refreshments in the cookbook. This would allow people to taste firsthand some of my recipes. Fortunately, many customers could have cared less about doing the food tasting at the time, as much as they wanted to support me. I was successful at mailing out a lot of books and a lot of VIP packages.

Though I couldn't execute the book tour as I had hoped, I did move forward with my book, but because of COVID, we did a virtual launch on April 25. My immediate family, mom, and several others were with me. The launch was much smaller than I had imagined. I was not able to sign books with people standing around me. However, when this next book is launched, I will also have some cookbooks available for purchase.

Brokenhearted

Mom was killed on July 6, 2020. That was an enormous loss for our family, and as to be expected with any tragedy, I was not prepared to live without my momma. She was the matriarch of our family and loved by many extending outside our bloodlines.

My mom was murdered by her granddaughter - my niece, my brother Charles' daughter Alisha. It's the stuff you see on the news, read in the newspapers, or see in the movies. I thought this happened to those other families, not mine! I never imagined I'd be mourning over the loss of my mother this way.

Momma played a crucial role in assisting me and my brother with raising our kids, so quite naturally, this was just as difficult for our kids as it was for me and my brother.

I was terribly heartbroken. My mom was my first best friend and my number one supporter. She would not be able to come to any more backyard parties, Sunday dinners, grand openings, or graduations. I miss her so much.

We thought we would grow old together like Blanche and Sophia from The Golden Girls. She was only 22 years older than me, and the way Scleroderma was stiffening my joints and slowing me down seemed like she was aging backward. She was getting around better than me.

We had just joked about this a few days before this tragedy. One day, she asked me if I had gotten out of bed yet. Had I taken my medicine? Had I eaten something yet? I responded, "Ma, stop doing that! I'm the daughter; I'm supposed to be the one checking on you!"

She said, "Well… I'm just checking on you because I love you!"

I wish she could ask me all the questions she wanted right about now. Routinely, when I'm stressed, I pray. When I'm grieving, I pray. When I'm sad, angry, scared, sick, depressed, or hopeless, I pray!

But at this moment, I was stuck on three letters to God, WHY? I could only muster the strength to ask God, "WHY?"

For more than a year, I was stuck. I couldn't form the words to pray. Nothing would come out. I tried praying out loud and to myself, but I had no words, only tears, and before I knew it, my hands were swollen, and I was experiencing heart palpitations.

I kept that heart flutter issue to myself until I was exposed via a trip to the ER. It was then that I discovered it was something called Esophageal Spasms. These spasms caused me to experience pain and flutter in my chest. That pain radiates to the back of my neck, jaw, throat, and sometimes my arms. You couldn't tell me I wasn't having a heart attack! But no, it was more like a stress attack.

I thought God was punishing me. I was trying to figure out what or whom I could have done so wrong that this was my punishment on top of being diagnosed with a vicious disease that snatched away something I loved doing so much.

Since then, I have learned that my niece was and is struggling with mental health issues, and her actions were probably influenced by her misuse of synthetic drugs, mushrooms, and vaping, which she got involved with at the age of seventeen. I also found out that prior to her murdering my mom, she had been diagnosed with Bipolar 1, a type of mental illness. This disorder can cause your mood to swing from an extreme high to an extreme low. Manic symptoms can include increased energy, excitement, impulsive behavior, hypomania, and agitation. I'm unsure what triggered Alisha, but the results were a total loss for all closest to my mom. She was sentenced to 20 years in prison with the possibility of parole after 13 years.

Mo The Realtor

I went from being trapped in the house to wanting to get back outside with a purpose: selling real estate.

Twenty years ago, I did not pass the state real estate exam in South Carolina, so I let go of that goal after trying three times! My mom was really proud of me for wanting to be a real estate agent. She thought that was a "fancy job." She used to brag to everyone that I would be a real estate agent. With a smile, I would correct her and say that I was only in school and was not yet an agent.

After COVID, I had been missing my mom, and there were times during my down episodes when I remembered how proud she was of me for wanting to be an agent, so I decided to go to real estate school. I signed up for classes via Zoom in January of 2021.

Then I got COVID just three days later. It wasn't easy to attend the classes. I was so sick; sometimes, I could not hold myself up. I was not able to continue that session. I started again with another series of virtual classes in May. That did not work out in my favor because I did not pass the classroom test to advance to the opportunity to take the state exam. Then I decided to attend a physical in-person class in November and did much better. I'm a verbal learner anyway.

I passed the class exam and was ready to take the state exam. Due to my disability with Raynaud's, I easily get cold, so I must always be prepared with gloves and a jacket. Those things are not allowed in a testing site unless you have a disability for special privileges. I'm also dyslexic and must read most things out loud for comprehension. The testing site allowed me to take the test in a private room so I could read out loud. After three failures, I passed the exam on the fourth try.

In 2022, I passed the real estate exam, and it's been ongoing learning ever since. I've been taking a lot of continuing education classes while at the same time prospecting for new clients. Feeling motivated to succeed, I wanted to complete something that I did not finish when I was younger, and I did it. Mission accomplished.

My mom had already given me so much praise, telling people how proud she was of me for my accomplishment, so I needed to do that for us. I just wanted to hear "Job well done" or "I'm proud of you" from my mom.

My goal is to build my clientele and help as many families as I can achieve their goals of becoming a homeowner.

Please call me if you or anyone you know wants to purchase a home in Georgia or South Carolina. You can find me on Facebook, @Motherealtor, on IG @MoTheRealtor22 or call me at 404-857-7675 (yep... my book, my "Shameless Plug") lol

"Homeownership is possible y'all. Let's talk Mo about it!"

TODAY

Today, my career is going in a different direction than my vision.

I want to become an advocate and encourage others not to shelter behind Scleroderma or any other sickness they might be battling.

I am still relevant. I'm still here. I've been rerouted. And I can still see my name in the lights; I'm just on a different path than the one I was on earlier in my life. I feel like God is using me as a physical vessel to be visible for people to see and vocal for people to hear my message about Scleroderma.

I was determined to continue my post-secondary education after high school. I wanted more choices and more economic opportunities than I had growing up. My determination comes from within me; my inner motivation grows every time I hear **NO!**

Evolving

Each person brings their coping skills to their life situation. I had to learn how to cope with Scleroderma. It is a lot, and it ain't for the faint of heart. Here are a few that were relevant to me while on my journey:

Be Honest. Being honest about what I could and could not do was extremely important. Of course, getting to this place of being honest with myself took a while. But by being honest, I laid the foundation for knowing what I needed help with and how, to be honest with those around me.

Moving Forward. It is imperative to be able to move forward with your life. My style was not to complain. When I was asked, "How are you doing?" I would respond that I was good. When someone would try to help me get up, I would respond that I got it, I don't need any help. When I would say that, they did not know how difficult it was for me. They did not know how to empathize with my situation.

I often thought about my mom's car accident that paralyzed her for over a year. The doctors told her she would never walk again, but her faith was strong, plus I had a praying grand momma. Despite what the doctors said, Momma walked again and worked for more than 30 years after the diagnosis.

Those memories gave me hope. I often pray for that same kind of miracle. Some people with Scleroderma go into remission and go on to live their best lives. So, I began making the transition in my thinking, going from being angry that this happened to me to "I'm happy to be alive."

Keep Learning. It is a continuous learning process and educating myself about Scleroderma and how it affects me. Take responsibility for educating your loved ones about what you are going through. Let people know your limitations and inform the people around you about your current situation. I set expectations for my family to understand what can happen to me, a patient with Scleroderma. I am a person with skin tightening. People can see the joint stiffness but can't see my muscle pain, so I can't assume they know that without my explaining it to them. You are not looking for a pity party, but others must try to understand what we are going through. We don't want pity; we want understanding and some awareness.

Self-Encouragement. I was living differently and more affirming about what was going on. I encouraged myself and even encouraged others to continue pressing on. My mantra is "I am an overcomer!"

Listen and Make Changes. I decided the doctors might know more about this medicine than me. Ha. So, I decided to listen. I decided to stop skipping my meds. I stopped throwing those tantrums within myself. I did get with the program, but it took some time.

Recognize your Progress. Pay attention to how you are doing and try to take pleasure in your progress. Give yourself credit where it is due.

I DECIDED

Facing physical challenges has been difficult. Especially when I've never been sick before. In 2021, after more than a year of being unable to talk to God due to grief, anger, hurt, and emotional distress, I found my voice and prayed again. For starters, I wanted to know, "How do I get out of this routine, this pattern of self-doubt? How do I get out of my own way?"

When I began to pray, I pleaded, "More of you, God, and less of me; please show me the way. In God's time, he began to show me that it was time to come out of my routine of sadness, frustration, and depression. God assured me, it won't always be like this. He had a "New thing" that he wanted me to step into, but I had to have Peace in my heart before I received the Position because it's difficult to be promoted to the next level when you are holding on to so much pain.

I arrived at a place where I began to love myself and my life again. God showed me that it's not so much about me learning to love my life again as much as it is, having the mindset, not about what's going to happen, but whatever happens should make me better. If God allows something to show up in my life, it must be designed to be a teacher to me. Only he can perfect all things concerning me. That said, I began to use my time to pray for others needing prayer. I stood in the gap for believers near and far, praying for their healing, blessings, and deliverance.

I felt that God was about to exchange my trauma for my testimony. It was time for me to thank God and give him the Glory despite what was going on with me, "Glory to God!" I needed to sit still and be faithful while fasting, believing, and praying that I was next in line for my miracle. They say there is no cure for Scleroderma, but Mark 5:34 reads, *"Daughter, your faith has made you well go in peace, and be healed of your disease."*

Healing is a contact sport. You have to be all in when you are expecting your miracle. You get no warning when it's going to happen; you have to be continuously working on yourself inside and outside, mind, body, and spirit. I had to dig deep to find new happiness. Since COVID changed the world, I stopped attending physical church and adopted worshiping at home or wherever I chose when I needed spiritual guidance. I discovered that there was a process to finding internal happiness as well.

First, you must own your happiness. Don't count on anyone else to make you happy. Be responsible for bringing Joy and Peace into your heart. It's up to no one else. The tighter my skin got, the more my arms began to curl, and my range of motion decreased significantly. I turned into a shopaholic. I saw Amazon, FedEx, and DHL in heavy rotation. Marvin began complaining about all the clothes I was buying, but I was trying to find pieces to cover my arms, camouflage the permanently bent arm I had become ashamed of, and still be cute. Y'all know I'm a bit of a fashionista! I was extremely self-conscious about how dark my skin had gotten and how noticeable the scar tissue was.

Second, challenge your own story. Change how you talk to yourself about who you are and what you want to do with your life. People often torment themselves by how they see themselves. For example, when I was 252 pounds, I wanted to be smaller because I was insecure about being "thicker than a snicker." I often disguised the lack of security as confidence and loving the skin I was in, but I stayed on some kind of diet. I often wondered if my husband looked at other women with admiration differently than he looked at me.

After the weight loss from the gastric sleeve surgery, Scleroderma attacked and I continued to lose weight, plummeting to 120lbs. Well, guess what? I wasn't happy there either! I thought I looked sick and worried terribly about what people saw when they looked at me. I realized that no diet, amount of clothes, the number on the scale, or the size of jeans I wear would make me feel better about myself if I did not deposit positivity into how I treated myself daily.

Lastly, enjoy the journey to happiness. Don't just be focused on the destination and omit enjoying and learning from every step of the process. Don't just wait to celebrate success when you finish; celebrate along the way.

I began to be intentional about improving my mental, dietary, and physical health. In addition to prayer and meditation, I started incorporating affirmations into my daily routine. When I began to speak positively to myself at the start of my day, it carried me throughout the day. When I changed the foods I ate, my mood, blood pressure, and energy improved significantly. When I incorporated physical therapy on a regular schedule, I gained a little Mo pep in my steps one day at a time.

I spent many nights crying myself to sleep, asking God, Why Me? Holding on to Psalm 30:5 that weeping may endure for a night, but joy comes in the morning. It took a while for me to receive this kind of joy, but I woke up one morning and said to God, "Why not me?" I realized God chose me for this position. He didn't sentence me with pain; He trusted me with this assignment. Who did I think I was, resisting when He wanted to use me? Then, I realized God was preparing me for what He has for me. He has continuously shown me my name in lights which is apparently my end. Visions are a glimpse of your end. That's called the plan between your destiny and where you are now. The plan is the process that takes you to your destination. During that time, God takes you through different changes to develop you. Character, patience, stewardship, and obedience get you righteous for those ordered steps. I asked God for strength, and He gave me difficulties to strengthen me. I asked for courage, and God gave me dangers to overcome. I asked for love, and God sent me troubled people to help. *But who was assigned to help me,* I thought.

My healing began when I DECIDED that my scars were seeds. I decided to let the word of God water them, and I will allow my children's children to eat from the fruits of the scars that should have taken me out of here, which is why I wrote this book. The suffering I've endured made a demand on what God placed inside of me, and I decided there is power on the other side of my suffering. Suffering is not the end; this is my breakthrough!

I release the power of love to heal all of our scars. Your scars may be different from mine, but today in this very moment, Faith is working for us. Together, let us embrace the scars that remind us of the triumphs, the victories—the scars did not stop us; we will win in the name of Jesus! The glass is not half empty; it's half full! Our perspective allows us to receive the power waiting to ignite and heal others through our stories! Take this journey with me, heal with me, and evolve with me.

CONCLUSION

Wow, as this part of our time together closes, I want to thank you for taking this journey with me. Writing this book was genuinely therapeutic. I can't wait to share my powerful discoveries in the next book. You are in my heart, and I want you to promise to stop soaking in the pain. I decided that Scleroderma would not write my story. It wasn't easy to move past the pain, but I'm so glad I stopped soaking in it. I started creating memories that continue to fuel my engine!

Listen, my mama used to intentionally offer ways to get me out of the house, off the couch, and away from the horror thoughts and fears racing in my head. I would decline her invitation. I'd say, "No, Ma, I'm tired, I can't walk that far, I don't feel good...." I believed everything the clinical definition of Scleroderma said applied to me, and it was as if I was waiting on those things to take me out. Just as your imagination can illuminate the worst, your imagination can create dreams and visions of defeating Scleroderma or whatever has caused chaos in your life. We get to decide, live, and manage our circumstances. Take back your power; you decide!

Make memories in every imaginable way and leave your imprint on this life. What legacy do you want to leave behind? I take pictures, travel, laugh, and release my love! Mama understood that life is to be lived, no matter what.

I got up and decided to take my cards and play them according to the mindset of Mo! I was born to stand under the lights. However, I had to change my perspective and mindset to overcome life's most challenging times.

Manifestation is real. Try those daily positive affirmations I spoke of, then check yourself after 30 days. If you believe, they will believe. I've always been Loud, Bold, and Intentional, so "this little light of mine, I'm going to let it shine" until I expire. Believe in yourself; get up!

We were born to meet the moment designed to catapult us with a testimony. That moment may have been introduced to you disguised as a blessing, a traumatic experience, a health issue, or even the loss of a loved one, but in the Bible, Romans 8:28 says, "If God brings you to it, he will help you get through it. Your testimony comes from your tests. Stop soaking in the pain. God got you.

I've provided a few pages designed for your notes at the back of the book. Please, share your story, comments, or messages. I'd love to hear from you. I've included my email and information so you can stay in touch with the Mo Experience.

I appreciate your support of The Mo Experience. May God add a blessing to the reading of these words.

ACKNOWLEDGEMENTS

Thank you to all the doctors, nurses, aids, and medical staff who helped me throughout my diagnosis. It hasn't been easy, and God knows I have not been the easiest patient every visit, but your knowledge and passion for your profession emanate in how you care for your patients; for that, I am eternally grateful.

Dr. Yvonne Smith has been setting the highest standards of excellence in internal medicine and pediatrics for over 30 years. Her current practice is **Rophe Adult & Pediatric Medicine**, **www.rophemed.com**, located at **4910 Jonesboro Rd, Union City, GA 30291**

Dr. Katina Tsagaris, MD, is a rheumatology specialist in Atlanta, GA. Dr. Tsagaris has extensive experience in Osteoporosis & Screening and Arthritis & Arthropathy. She is affiliated with medical facilities such as Emory University Hospital and Emory University Hospital Midtown.

Dr. Camilla Nelson earned her medical degree from Albert Einstein College of Medicine in New York. She is currently practicing at 483 Upper Riverdale Rd. SW, Ste. C, Riverdale, GA 30274

Dr. Richard Silver is a professor of medicine and pediatrics and has been director of the Division of Rheumatology and Immunology since 1995. **2125 Charlie Hall Blvd, Charleston, SC 29414**

Dr. DeAnna Baker Frost is an adult rheumatologist with a clinical interest in autoimmune diseases and fibrosis. A native of Baltimore, MD, she completed a combined M.D. and Ph.D. program at MUSC and an internal medicine residency at Duke University. Her office is 5500 Front St., Suite 320, Summerville, South Carolina, 29483.

Dr. Agnes Han, MD, is a gastroenterology specialist in Atlanta, GA, and has over 27 years of experience in the medical field. Dr. Han has extensive experience in Gastrointestinal Disorders. She graduated from the City University Of New York / Medical School In 1995. She is currently practicing at **960 Johnson Ferry Rd, Atlanta, GA 30342**

Dr. Michael Chen is a native of Milledgeville, GA. He graduated valedictorian from Baldwin High School in 1997 and afterward attended The University of Georgia for his undergraduate degree in Biology. **http://dentaloflithonia.com**
The business is located at **7660 COVINGTON Highway, LITHONIA, GA 30058**

Dr. Ali John Zarrabi, MD, Hospice and palliative medicine internal medicine at Emory Clinic located at 1365 Clifton Rd. Bldg. A., Atlanta, GA 30322.

Dr. Harini Naidu, MD, is a gastroenterology specialist in Atlanta with over 11 years of experience in the medical field. She graduated from Boston University in 2011. She specializes in Gastroenterology and is currently at Emory Clinic, 1365 Clifton Rd Atlanta, Ga 30322.

Ijeoma Isiadinso, MD MPH FACC FASNC, is a Board-Certified Cardiologist at the Emory Heart and Vascular Center and Assistant Professor of Medicine (Cardiology) at Emory University School of Medicine. Dr. Isiadinso is the Medical Director of the Emory Preventive Cardiology Program. She joined the faculty at Emory University School of Medicine in 2010. She is Board-Certified in General Cardiology, Nuclear Cardiology, and Echocardiography, currently at Emory Clinic, located at 1365 Clifton Rd Atlanta, Ga 30322.

Dr. Ashley Michelle Rogers is an Anesthesiology Specialist in Atlanta, Georgia. She graduated with honors in 2012. Having more than 11 years of diverse experiences, especially in ANESTHESIOLOGY, Dr. Ashley Michelle Rogers affiliates with many hospitals, including Emory University Hospital, Emory University Hospital Midtown, Emory Johns Creek Hospital, cooperates with many other doctors and specialists in the medical group, The Emory Clinic, Inc

Dr. Mercy Amua-Quarshie, MD OB-GYN Board-Certified Obstetrician and Gynecologist since 2001, was originally born in Ghana, West Africa, but grew up in NY, where she received her medical degree from New York University School of Medicine in 1995, and then went on to residency training in OB GYN at Boston Medical Center/Boston University. She practices at Dekalb Women's Specialists, **www.dekalbwomen.com,1458 Church St Unit B, Decatur, GA 30030**.

Dr. Straughn has advanced training, experience in African American skin, and expertise in treating all skin hues and hair textures. She thoroughly understands the sensitivities associated with treating keloids, melasma, vitiligo, and ingrown hair. She is an active member of the **Skin of Color Society.** She is currently located at Buckhead Dermatology, **2961 Hardman Ct NE, Atlanta, GA 30305 www.buckheaddermatology.com**

Photographer Jayvon Hilton
Von Wick Visuals **five5von@gmail.com** IG @vonotjohn

Thank you to Dr. Brunetta Nelson and the talented team at Imprint Productions, Inc. who helped create this book.

Please subscribe to my YouTube channel @Teal Talk with Mo to continue to follow my journey.

Notes

Notes

Notes

Notes

Notes

Milton Keynes UK
Ingram Content Group UK Ltd.
UKHW010813081123
432193UK00005B/379